ON TRACK
READERS FOR ADULT STUDENTS

Julio

Penny Cameron
Language & Culture Center
University of Houston

Heinle & Heinle Publishers
A Division of Wadsworth, Inc.
Boston, Massachusetts 02116 U.S.A.

Acknowledgments

The author wishes to thank the following people
for their help and advice:

Esperanza Fitch

Christine Fuentes

Angel German

Benjamin Griffith

Mary Jo Moore

Bob Pollock

Sheila Sullivan

Kathryn Vidal

Janet Waites

Publisher: Stanley J. Galek
Editorial Director: Christopher Foley
Assistant Editor: Margaret Morris
Editorial Production Manager: Elizabeth Holthaus
Manufacturing Coordinator: Lisa McLaughlin
Design and Composition: PC&F, Inc.
Cover Design and Illustration: Cyndy Patrick

10 9 8 7 6 5 4 3 2 1

ISBN 0-8384-2928-9

Heinle & Heinle Publishers is a division of Wadsworth, Inc.

Manufactured in the United States of America

Contents

Introduction

These stories are about people who are new to America. They have problems, but they overcome them. The things they learned in other places help them. And, because they're adults, they can say, "We know that!"

People learn how to do things in one place or country. When they leave, they take what they know with them. They don't forget what they already know.

Please read these stories, and think about what you already know. Use your knowledge to help you. It doesn't matter where you learned what you know!

Mrs. Lau is a grandmother. She comes to live with her son and his family. But she doesn't feel at home. Still, she wants to be with her son's children, and they're in America. Most grandmothers want to be with their grandchildren. Mrs. Lau is wise. She likes to help people, and she finds her place in America. She uses what she knows.

Julio Martinez comes from Mexico. He's learning new things all the time. When he starts to learn English, his life gets much better. He falls in love. Then things go wrong. Julio listens to another student in his class. Her experience helps him decide what to do.

Valentina Petrov comes from Russia. It's easy for her to get work, but she doesn't like her job. She loses her baby; then her marriage ends. Valentina uses what she knows from her old country. That's how she builds her new life in her new country.

Antonio Chirinos comes from Venezuela. He's a trainee in a store. He's learning about sales. Antonio already knows how to sell things because he worked in a store in his own country. A good salesperson is a good salesperson everywhere. Antonio's skill helps him to live in America. His driving experience in Caracas also helps him late one night.

To the Student

If you are reading on your own, please follow these steps:

1. Think about the title of the book or chapter. What does it mean?
2. Before you read a chapter, look at the pictures. What do you see?
3. Try to answer the **Before You Read** questions. Use your dictionary if you need help.
4. If you have the cassette tape, play it. Listen to the story. Read the story while you listen to the tape. Don't use the dictionary.
5. Play the tape and listen to the story again. Use your dictionary if you don't understand some words.
6. Play the tape and read aloud along with it. Try to copy the voice on the tape.
7. Answer the **After You Read** questions. Write notes for questions 3 and 4 if you're working alone. Write a longer answer for question 5.

Answers to the **After You Read** exercises 1 and 2 appear in the instructor's manual for this book. Ask your teacher for a copy of the manual if you don't have it. No answers are given for exercises 3, 4, and 5. For those exercises, many different answers are correct.

JULIO

Chapter 1

What's Best for Julio?

Before You Read

1. **Discuss these questions with your classmates:**
   - What big decision did you once make? How did you feel?

   Use your own words, or choose words from this list:

confident	excited	frightened
happy	nervous	worried

2. **Look at the picture on the previous page. Julio is in the corner of his mother's house in Mexico. His brothers and sisters are sitting around the table talking. Think about the picture and answer these questions:**
   - Why is Julio all by himself?
   - How does everyone feel? What happened?

3. **Look at the picture on page 2. Julio is with his brothers near the Rio Grande. Manuel is holding some American money. Tomas is giving Julio a package. Match the numbers on the picture with the words below:**

   _____ brooch   _____ package

   _____ cliff   _____ Rio Grande

   _____ Manuel   _____ Tomas

   _____ Julio

4. **Think about the picture and answer these questions:**
   - Why are they at the Rio Grande?
   - How old is Julio?
   - Is Tomas the same age as Julio?

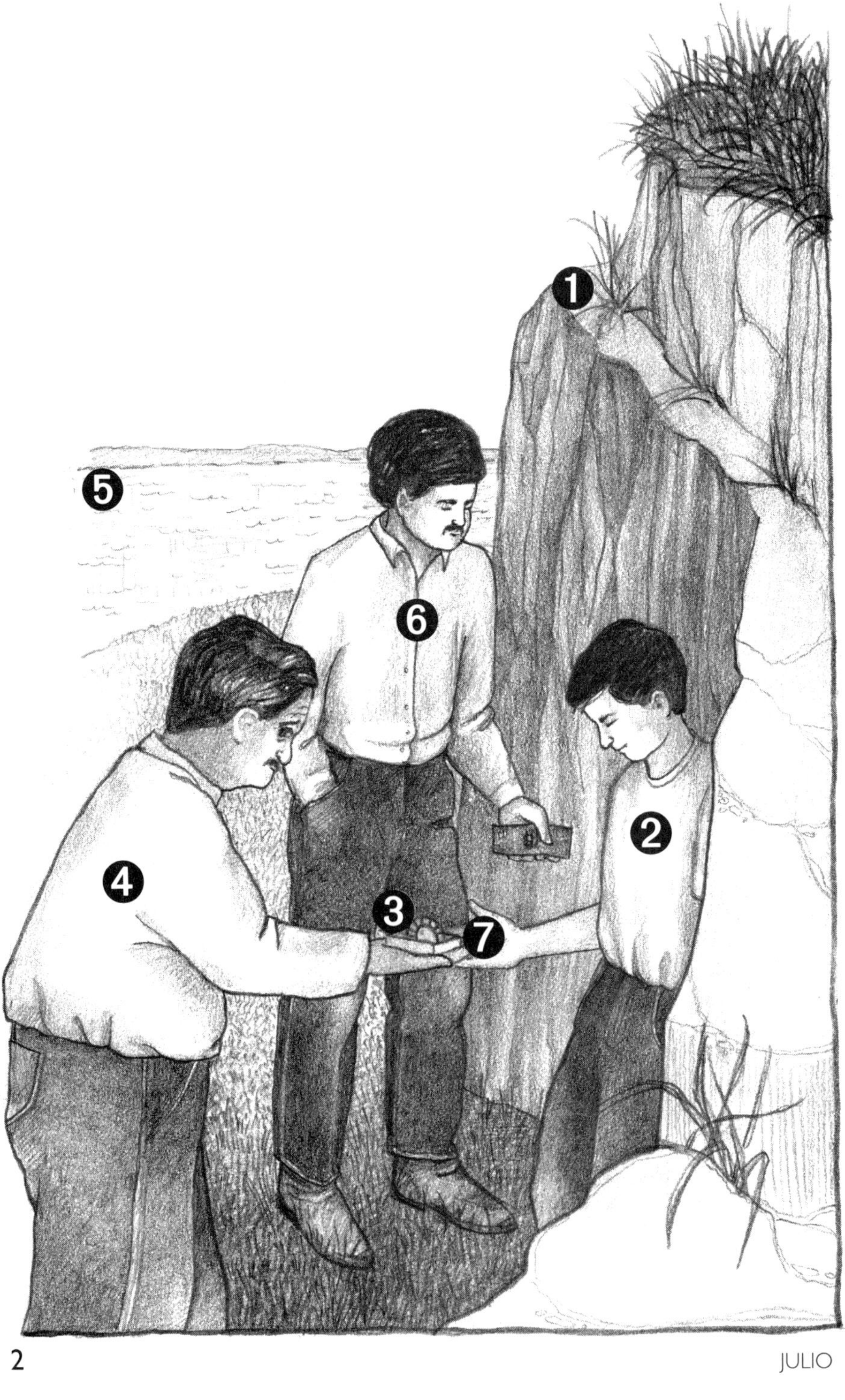
1
2
3
4
5
6
7

What's Best for Julio?

Julio Martinez sits in a corner in his mother's home in Coahuila State, Mexico. His brothers and sisters are sitting around a table. He can hear their voices. He knows they are talking about him, but he doesn't care. His mother is dead. She died a week before.

Julio is seventeen and the youngest in the family, the baby. Julio's next brother, Manuel, is thirty-three years old. The eldest brother, Tomas, is forty-four years old. There are two other brothers, Raul and Jairo, and two sisters, Carmen and Francisca.

Tomas speaks quietly. He doesn't want Julio to hear him.

"What are we going to do?" he asks. "I have five children of my own. I can give Julio a place to sleep, but that's all. There's not enough work for me to give him a job."

Manuel looks worried. "Rosa and I have to look after our kids, too," he says. "I wish we could keep him with us, but we can't. His chances are better with Francisca."

"You mean in San Angelo, in America?" Carmen asks.

"In America," Manuel replies. "Francisca has been in Texas for ten years now. She has no children. She can take Julio."

"But America is so far away," Tomas worries.

"Life is good in America," Manuel says. "It's very difficult for us to go. We have children. But Julio is young and strong. Francisca can help him."

"Francisca is happy in America," Carmen says. "But she moves around a lot, you know. Things are often difficult for her. She couldn't even come home for Mama's funeral."

"Well, what do you suggest?" Manuel asks. He wants answers, not questions. "What can you offer him?"

Tomas leans back in his chair. "Let's ask Julio what he wants to do," he says. "If he wants to stay here, we'll find a place for him. And if he wants to go to Francisca, we'll send him to America."

"And if the American police catch him? What then?" Carmen asks.

"They'll send him back to Mexico," Tomas says. "But don't worry. I know a man who goes into Big Bend Park. His name is Jorge Mendoza. He sells things to the American tourists there. Jorge often takes people across the river to the United States."

Manuel gets up from the table and goes to Julio. He puts his hand on his younger brother's shoulder.

"Come join us," he says gently. Julio follows him to the table.

All day Julio has felt strange. Things aren't quite real. He seems to be talking to people through glass.

Julio sits next to Tomas. Tomas puts an arm on his shoulder and asks, "What do you want to do, Julio? Do you want to stay here?"

Julio shakes his head. He knows the answer to that question. Tomas will bring his family to live in the house. There won't be room for Julio to live there, too.

Manuel asks, "Do you know what you want to do?"

Julio looks down. He wants his mother back again. But that's not possible.

"Would you like to go to Francisca in America?" Manuel asks.

Julio thinks about it. He knows very little about America. He hardly remembers Francisca. He knows what she looks like from the photographs. Sometimes Francisca sent money and photos to Mama. In the pictures, Francisca is always smiling and laughing. Julio makes up his mind.

"I want to go to America," he tells Manuel. "It will be an adventure," he thinks to himself.

He makes his voice sound big and confident. But inside he feels small and a little frightened.

Four weeks later, Manuel, Tomas, and Julio are standing near a cliff. They're looking across the Rio Grande. America is on the other side of the river. Soon a man with a boat will come.

Tomas opens a small package. "This is Mama's gold brooch," he says. Tomas, Manuel, and Julio look at the brooch. It's a small circle of gold. Tomas hands it to Julio. "Give it to Francisca," he says.

Manuel gives Julio some cash: $26 in American money.

Tomas says, "I wrote to Francisca. I told her to meet you at about 4:00 P.M. in the parking lot near the river." He pauses. "We don't have her answer yet. Do you still want to go?"

Julio stands up tall. "You keep asking me that," he says. "Of course, I want to go. Francisca's letter is probably waiting at our village right now. I told you, don't worry."

Tomas looks worried anyway.

"I'm seventeen," Julio says. "I know where San Angelo is, and I have Francisca's address. I'm ready to go." He looks down the beach. He can see a boat coming quietly toward them. There are two men in it. "Is that it?"

"Yes," Tomas replies. "That's the boat. Go on, little brother. Your adventure is about to begin."

After You Read

1. Write *T* if the statement is true and *F* if it's false. If the statement is false, write the true answer below it.

__F__ 1. There's plenty of work for Julio in Mexico.
There isn't enough work for Julio.

_____ 2. Julio's mother is dead.

_____ 3. Julio is part of a small family.

_____ 4. Julio's sister Francisca lives in Mexico.

_____ 5. Tomas is worried about Julio.

2. Complete each sentence with one of the words below:

adventure	confident
eldest	funeral
gently	makes up his mind
suggest	tourists

1. His ___**eldest**___ brother Tomas is forty-four years old. He's older than the others.

2. Julio is trying something new and unknown. It's an

   __________ .

3. When Julio's mother died, Francisca couldn't come

   home for the __________ .

4. "Well, what do you __________ ? Do you have another idea for us?"

5. Manuel speaks softly. "Come join us," he says

   __________ .

6. Julio decides to go to America. He __________ to go there.

7. Julio tries to sound sure of himself, or __________ . He wants Tomas to think he isn't worried.

8. __________ often visit different countries or places.

3. Look over Chapter 1 and answer the questions below.

- What do you know about Tomas?

____

____

____

- What do you know about Francisca?

4. **Discuss these questions with your classmates. Make notes on what you decide.**
   - Where is Julio's father? Why do you think so?

5. **How does Julio feel when he leaves his brothers? Have you ever felt that way? Tell the class, or write a story. OR: Do you know someone who left home? Did you help that person? How? Tell the class, or write a story about your experience.**

Chapter 2

Big Bend

Before You Read

1. **Discuss these questions with your classmates:**
   - Will it be easy for Julio to live in America?
   - What does "wetback" mean?
   - Will Francisca be there to meet Julio? Why do you think so?
   - What will Julio do while he's waiting?

   With the rest of the class, discuss the things Julio might do:

hide	swim in the river
play	talk to people

2. **Look at the picture on page 8. Julio is hiding in a cave. Think about the picture and answer these questions:**
   - Why is Julio in the cave?
   - How does he feel?

3. **Look at the picture on page 10. Julio is climbing into the back of a pickup truck. Match the numbers on the picture with the words and phrases below:**

   _____ pickup truck   _____ bumper sticker

   _____ blanket

4. **Think about the picture and answer these questions:**
   - Why is Julio climbing into the pickup truck?
   - Where is the truck going?

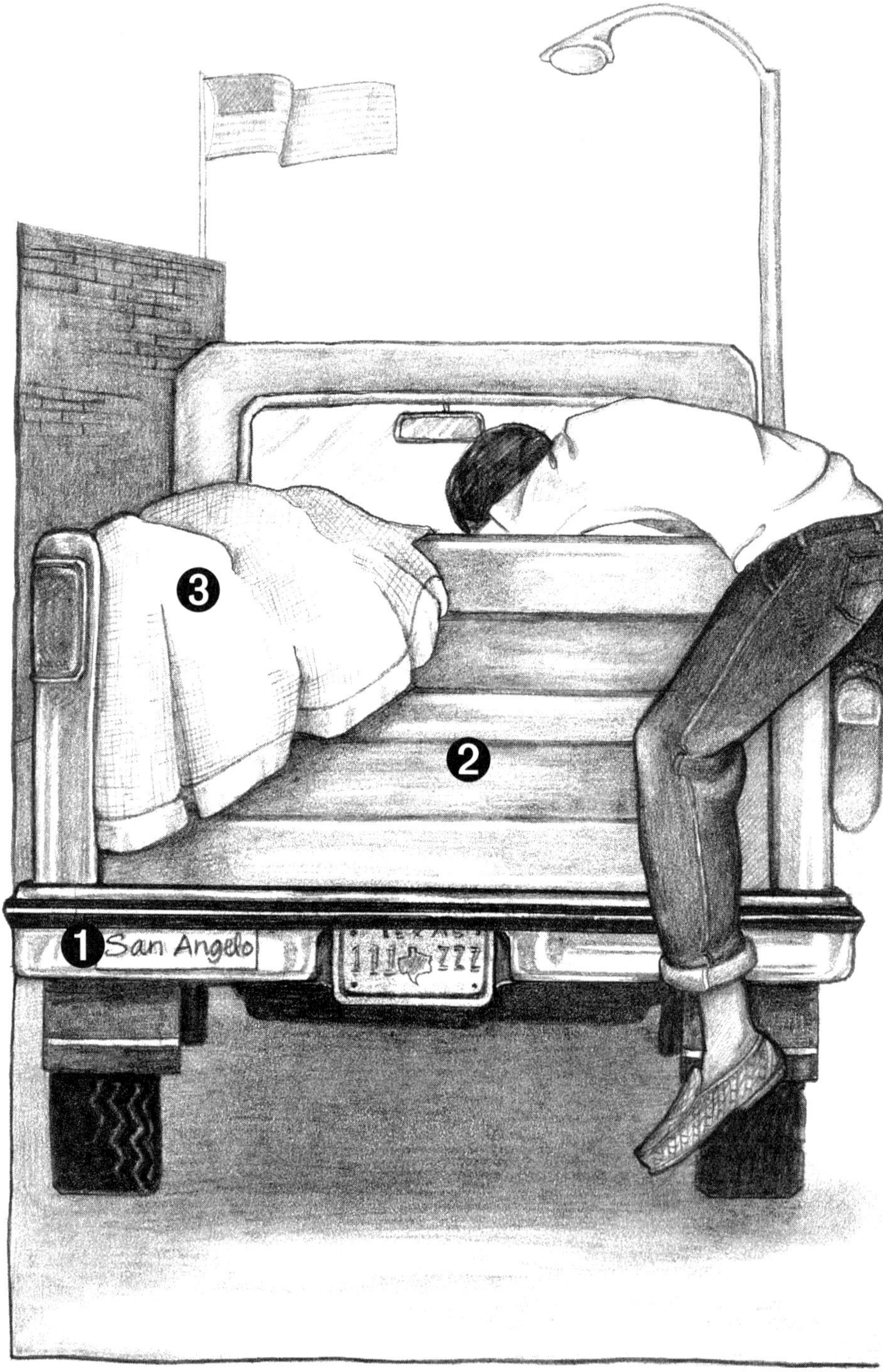
1
San Angelo
2
3

Big Bend

Julio sits in the boat without speaking. Tomas and Manuel are gone. In just a few minutes, he'll be in America.

The boat runs up the shore. Julio and Jorge Mendoza jump out. Jorge is carrying some things to sell to tourists. The man with the boat starts back across the Rio Grande.

"When will your sister come?" Jorge asks.

"About four," Julio replies.

"Stay out of the way," Jorge says. "There'll be a lot of tourists here soon. School is out now, so you'll see a lot of kids. Try not to get caught. And remember: You don't know me." He walks away quickly.

Julio feels excited. He's here, in America! He looks around. So far, it's just like the other side of the river.

He finds his way to the parking lot. Things look very clean and tidy. The signs are in English. He's really in America!

Julio checks the parking lot carefully. Tomas said to go to the north end. It's a good place to meet someone. It's still very early in the morning, but already people are moving around. Everybody is busy. Nobody will notice him.

Julio goes back to the beach to throw stones. A couple of boys, about fourteen or fifteen years old, are standing nearby. He listens to them talking. They're speaking Spanish, but it sounds different. It's not like Mexican Spanish. He moves a little closer to hear what they're saying.

"What are you listening to?" the older boy asks. Julio doesn't understand. The boy speaks again, this time in Spanish. "What are you listening to?"

"Nothing, nothing," Julio says. He moves away.

"Where did you come from?" the boy asks, stepping closer. He seems suddenly interested. Does he think that Julio came across the river illegally?

Julio doesn't answer.

"He's a wetback," the younger boy says. "Wetback! Wetback!" The boy runs across the beach to his father, a big Mexican American. The man returns with the boy.

"Where do you come from?" the man asks Julio in English.

Julio is afraid. He can't understand the words. The way the man speaks frightens him. The man sounds angry.

"Get away!" the man says in Spanish. "If I see you again, I'll call the police."

Julio looks up and down the beach. He sees some long grass at the far end. He rushes past the man and runs as fast as he can. His heart is beating hard. The man watches until Julio disappears from sight.

The boys' mother comes up. "Who was that?" she asks, pointing toward the grass.

"Some kid came across the river," the man says. "I told him I'd call the police."

"You probably scared him," his wife replies.

"Don't worry about him," the man says. "They're tough, those kids. He'll be all right. Anyway, I'm not going to call the police. I'm here on vacation!"

Julio is hiding in a cave. The long grass covers the entrance. Julio crawls farther inside the cave and sits down. His heart is still pounding. The adventure is not fun anymore.

Julio stays in the cave all morning. In the afternoon, he moves out carefully toward the parking lot. He finds a place where he can watch and wait for Francisca.

From three to four o'clock he waits. People come and go, but no one he knows. No one is looking for him.

At four o'clock he sees a woman. She looks a little like Francisca. He gets ready to greet her. But it's not Francisca. The woman doesn't really look like her at all.

At five o'clock, Julio is hungry and miserable. Where is Francisca?

At seven o'clock, Julio decides that his sister isn't coming. Maybe she didn't receive the letter. Maybe she's in trouble. What should he do? How will he get to San Angelo?

At eight, Julio wanders down to the parking lot. Very few cars are there now. Only one really interests him. It's an old pickup truck. It's parked near the entrance. A bumper sticker on the back of the truck reads "San Angelo."

Julio looks around. Nobody is watching, so he climbs into the back of the pickup. He slips under a pile of old blankets.

After about half an hour, Julio hears a man and a woman speaking English. They throw some things in the back of the pickup. Then they get into the front. Julio feels the truck start. He's on his way!

As the trucks bumps along, Julio looks out at the stars. The truck is traveling north. Julio feels happy. San Angelo is north and east of Big Bend.

Julio is hungry. He remembers Mama's tortillas. He tries not to think about food, and goes to sleep.

After You Read

1. Number these sentences in the correct order (1–6):

__2__ Julio listens to two Mexican American boys.

_____ Julio hides in the back of a pickup truck.

_____ The pickup travels north.

_____ Julio crosses the Rio Grande.

_____ Julio hides in a cave.

_____ The boys' father says that he'll call the police.

2. Match the words in column A with their meanings in column B.

A	B
1. notice	a. very sad
2. illegally	b. beating very hard
3. disappears	c. moves on hands and knees
4. crawls	d. against the law
5. pounding	e. goes where he cannot be seen
6. miserable	f. see

3. Circle the phrases (a, b, or c) closest in meaning to the underlined words and phrases below:

1. Stay out of the way.

   a. Don't let anyone see you.

   b. Go away!

   c. Let people see you.

2. It's just like the other side of the river.

   a. different from

   b. the same as

   c. not like

3. "They're tough, those kids."

   a. hardworking

   b. unfriendly

   c. not easily hurt

4. "I'm <u>on vacation</u>."

    a. working

    b. not working

    c. calling the police

5. He gets ready to <u>greet her</u>.

    a. say hello

    b. meet her

    c. shake her hand

4. What did Julio do while he was waiting for Francisca? Write your answer here.

____

____

____

____

____

____

5. Discuss the questions below with your classmates. Make notes on what you decide.

- Julio hid in a pickup truck. Was that a good idea?
- What else could Julio do?

6. Talk or write about the following question:

- What advice would you give to Julio?

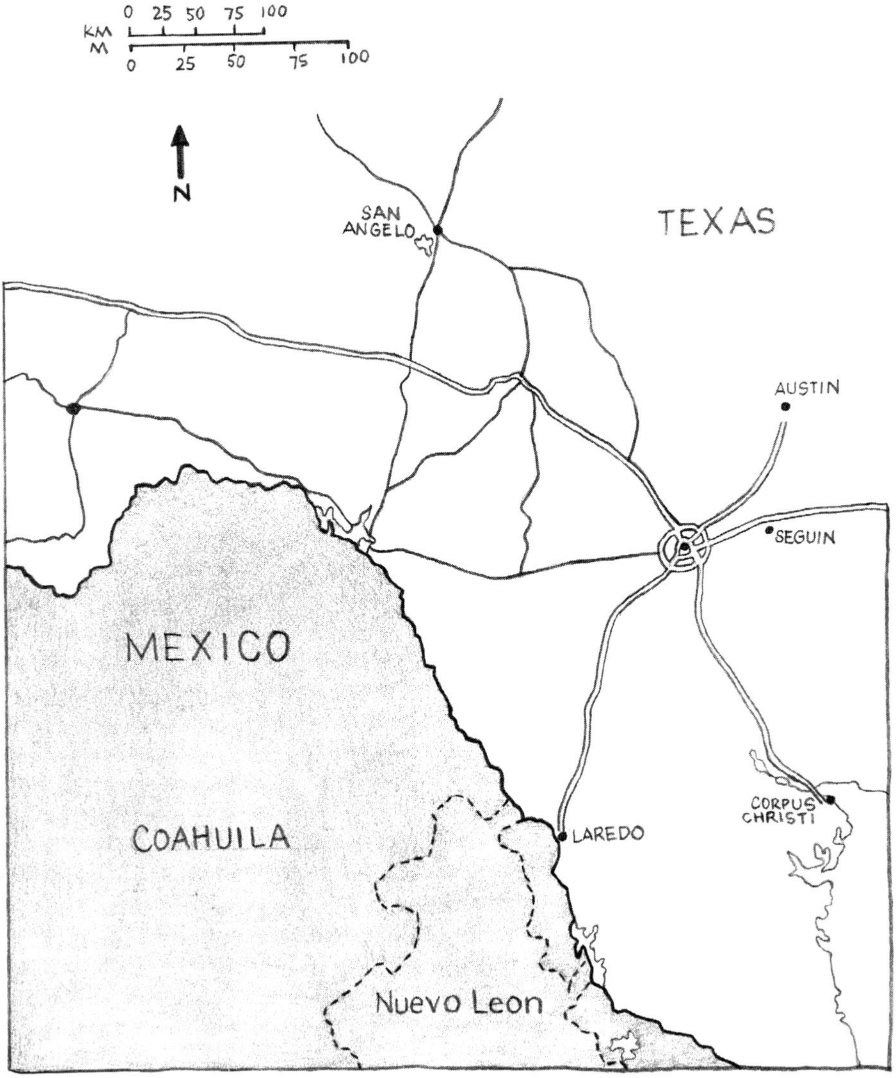
0 25 50 75 100
KM
M
0 25 50 75 100
N
SAN ANGELO
TEXAS
AUSTIN
SEGUIN
MEXICO
COAHUILA
LAREDO
CORPUS CHRISTI
Nuevo Leon

Chapter 3

The Trip to San Angelo

Before You Read

1. **Discuss these questions with your classmates:**
   - Will Julio find Francisca in San Angelo? Why do you think so?
   - What will Julio do if he can't find Francisca?
   - What's a delivery van?

2. **Look at the map on page 16. Think about the map and answer these questions:**
   - How far is it from Marathon to San Angelo?
   - Could you walk from Marathon to San Angelo?

3. **Look at the picture on page 18. Julio is in the coffee shop in Marathon. Match the numbers on the picture with the words below:**

   _____ menu

   _____ waitress

   _____ hamburger

   _____ apron

   _____ glass of milk

4. **Think about the picture and answer these questions:**
   - How does the waitress look?
   - How does Julio look?

   Use your own words, or choose words from this list:

amused	angry	kind
happy	hungry	tired
nervous	surprised	
worried	excited	

OPEN
MENU
1
2
3
4
5

The Trip to San Angelo

The truck drives along the road to Marathon. When it pulls off the road, Julio wakes up. He lies very still and waits.

The man and woman get out. Julio waits and listens for a few minutes. Then he climbs out of the truck. He rubs his eyes and looks around. Is this San Angelo?

Only one shop is open. The sign on the building reads "Marathon Coffee Shop," but Julio can't read it. He looks anxiously for the words "San Angelo." He can't find them.

The door of the coffee shop opens and Julio smells food. He remembers how hungry he is and goes in. The man and woman are there already. There are no other customers.

The waitress offers Julio a menu. Julio looks at it, but he can't read anything. He points to a number in the middle of the page.

"You don't want cornflakes at night, do you?" the waitress asks. She sounds surprised. Julio stays quiet.

The waitress takes the menu and turns it over. On the back there is a picture of a hamburger. She points to the hamburger. Julio smiles and says, "Si, si."

"I thought so," the waitress says. "Okay, let me see your money." She pulls a dollar bill out of the pocket of her apron. Then she holds her hand out.

Julio shows his money. She takes $4.00, and brings him a hamburger and a glass of milk. Julio eats and drinks very quickly. He's not fast enough.

The man and woman have finished their coffee. They're returning to the truck! Julio watches as they get in and drive away.

The waitress is looking at him again. Julio smiles and leaves the coffee shop.

Outside, Julio looks around for somewhere to sleep. He sees a few old houses across the road. They are dark inside. He walks around one house to make sure nobody is there. Then he lies down in a corner of the porch and falls asleep.

The next morning Julio finds a place to wash his face and hands. He's still tired, because he couldn't sleep properly. Mosquitoes bit him, and the floor was hard. Now he's stiff and uncomfortable.

Julio is hungry again. He decides to return to the coffee shop. The same waitress is there. This time she takes another $4.00 and shows him a picture of bacon and eggs. He eats everything she brings.

After the meal, Julio goes outside. He sees the waitress talking to a man. The man comes toward him.

"Should I run?" Julio wonders. "But where can I go?" He waits for the man to come to him.

"You're from Mexico," the man says in Spanish. It's a statement, not a question.

"Yes, sir," Julio replies.

"Where are you going?" the man asks. "You can't stay around here."

"San Angelo," Julio says. "I have a sister there."

"How will you get there?" the man asks.

"I need a ride," Julio says. "I don't have much money."

The man thinks for a minute. "Not many people go directly to San Angelo from here," he says. "Most people go somewhere else first. But you're in luck. A delivery van is coming through here today. It goes to San Angelo."

"That's great!" Julio says. "Which van do I look for?"

The man laughs. "That's easy!" he says. "Not much else comes through here. It's a blue van with gold letters on it. The driver usually parks over there." The man points behind the coffee shop.

The man pauses for a moment. "The driver can't take passengers," he adds, and walks away. There's no time for Julio to ask any questions.

Julio finds a place to sit. He can watch the coffee shop from there. No one can see him. He's bored. And it's very hard for him to say awake. At last, a blue van arrives.

Julio watches a man get out of the van. The man goes into the coffee shop. After a few minutes, he comes back out. He walks to the back of the van and opens it. Then he starts to unload some things.

When the man goes back into the coffee shop, Julio runs to the van. He climbs into the back with some boxes. He tries to hide himself behind some big ones.

The driver returns, takes something out, and closes the back of the van. Julio can't see, but he hears the driver get into the van. Then the front door slams shut and the motor starts.

Julio stays very quiet. It's a long drive. The man talks to himself and sings along with the radio. At last they stop. The driver opens the back of the van. Julio can just see the words "San Angelo" written on a storefront.

As soon as the driver walks away, Julio climbs out of the van and runs.

After a while, he comes to a gas station. He shows someone Francisca's address. The man points back down the road.

Two long hours later, Julio finds Francisca's house. He's hot and tired. He wants someone to talk to and feed him.

He knocks on the door. Nobody comes. He knocks again. Still no answer. He knocks loudly and yells in Spanish, "Francisca! Open up!"

A voice replies in Spanish, "She's not there."

After You Read

1. Circle the best word to complete each sentence.

Julio climbs out of the (1) (*truck van box*) in Marathon. He goes into the coffee shop and buys (2) (*some cornflakes a hamburger a cup of coffee*). He sleeps on the (3) (*porch corner door*) of an old house. A man tells him about a (4) (*road woman van*) going to San Angelo. The driver can't take (5) (*boxes passengers eggs*). Julio hides in the van and rides to (6) (*San Angelo Mexico Marathon*). He finds his sister's (7) (*road gas station house*), but she's not there.

2. Use these words from Chapter 3 to complete the sentences below:

anxiously	directly
mosquitoes	pulls off
slam	stiff
yells	

1. He searches __________ for the words "San Angelo." He's afraid he won't find them.
2. Small flying insects called __________ bite Julio.
3. Julio feels __________, and it's hard for him to move.
4. To go straight from one place to another without stopping is to go __________.
5. The truck __________ the side of the road and comes to a stop.
6. When you shut a door very hard, you __________ it.
7. Julio calls Francisca's name very loudly; he __________ it.

3. Write about Julio. Use your own words, or choose words from this list. Why does he feel this way?

anxious	hot	hungry
quiet	stiff	tired

Julio is anxious because he did not find Francisca

4. **Discuss the questions below with your classmates. Make notes on what you decide.**
   - How does the waitress feel about Julio? Was she kind to him? What did she do?
   - Why did she behave the way she did?

5. **Julio found his sister's house, but she wasn't there. Has anything like that ever happened to you? Tell the class, or write your story. OR: Pretend you are Julio. Ask a friend what to do. A classmate can be your friend and reply.**

1
2
3
4
5

Chapter 4

What Happened to Francisca?

Before You Read

1. **Discuss these questions with your classmates:**
   - Have you ever wanted something to happen that didn't happen? How did you feel?
   - What jobs do people have in a restaurant or diner?
   - What is the Immigration and Naturalization Service (INS)?

2. **What do these words mean? Which ones go together or are close in meaning?**

sad	disappointed	despondent
tired	exhausted	
upset	miserable	

3. **Look at the picture on page 24. Mrs. Mead is leading Julio in to see Alec Martin in the diner. Match the numbers on the picture with the words and phrases below:**

   _____ Mrs. Mead　　_____ Julio　　_____ diner

   _____ newspaper　　_____ Alec Martin

4. **Think about the picture and answer these questions:**
   - What kind of person is Mrs. Mead?
   - How does Julio feel?

What Happened to Francisca?

Julio turns around. An older woman is standing at the door of the next house. Julio walks slowly toward her.

"My dear child!" the woman says in Spanish. "You look exhausted! Sit down here. I'll get you something to drink." She hurries into the house and brings back a glass of water.

"Now," she says, "Tell me. Why are you here?"

Julio is almost too tired to talk. He feels like crying. But he tells the woman everything. He talks about his mother, Francisca, the letter, and the ride from Big Bend. He even talks about the mosquitoes.

When he stops, the woman says, "Your sister isn't here. They left very suddenly. I don't know why."

Julio doesn't know what to say. He never thought that Francisca would leave. He's very disappointed.

"My name's Anita Mead. I have their mail," the woman says. "Maybe your brother's letter never arrived." Mrs. Mead goes inside and returns with some envelopes.

Julio goes through the mail. Tomas's letter to Francisca is there, unopened.

"So that's why she didn't meet you!" Mrs. Mead says. "Your sister didn't know that you were coming."

Julio feels a little better. It wasn't Francisca's fault. She didn't leave him all alone on purpose. She simply didn't know he was coming.

"What are you going to do?" Mrs. Mead asks. "Do you have a job here in America?"

Julio feels frightened and hopeless. He has no job and no home in America.

The woman looks at him for a while. Then she says, "Maybe my brother Pedro can help you. He has a restaurant in Seguin. It's east of San Antonio. Some Mexican boys work for him. Can you work hard?"

"I'm a good worker," Julio answers quickly. "Will your brother take me?"

"I don't know," the woman says. "But you're lucky. Pedro is going to call me tonight. I'll tell him about you."

Julio thanks Mrs. Mead and goes to find a place to eat. After dinner, he has only $11 left. He must find a job soon!

When Julio returns to his sister's house, it is closed up. He tries to find a place to sleep nearby. Mrs. Mead hears him outside.

"Is that you, Julio?" Mrs. Mead calls.

"Yes, Mrs. Mead," Julio replies.

"Good," she says. She comes to the door. "I spoke to Pedro. He wants me to take you to a diner in town. A friend of his is driving through San Angelo. He'll be at the diner in about one hour."

Julio feels strange. He seems to have no control over his life. "What if Pedro is a bad man?" he thinks. But then the next question comes: "What else can I do?"

"Thank you, Mrs. Mead," he says.

Mrs. Mead drives Julio to the diner. Pedro's friend Alec Martin is already there. He's sitting at a table reading a newspaper.

"I want to leave after I eat," he tells Julio. "Wait over there, near the door."

Julio obeys. Alec Martin looks bad-tempered. Julio doesn't want to argue with him, but he's worried. "What's going to happen now?" he thinks. He feels safe with Mrs. Mead. But very soon she'll say good-bye and go home.

After dinner, Alec Martin takes Julio to his car. Together they drive to Seguin. Alec doesn't speak to Julio again.

It's after midnight when they arrive. Alec pulls up in front of a small restaurant. He tells Julio to get out. There's a room at the back of the building.

"Go down there," he says. "You'll find some other kids. You'll meet Pedro at the restaurant in the morning."

Julio follows his instructions. His new life in Seguin is about to begin.

The years pass quietly. Julio is still working for Pedro Vazquez in Seguin.

One day Julio asks for more money.

"You know I can do all the jobs in the restaurant," Julio says.

"You can't wait tables," Pedro says. "You can't speak English. So, you can't work outside the kitchen."

"I can do lots of other jobs," Julio says. "Look at all the heavy work I do."

Julio is a good worker. Pedro knows that. He doesn't want Julio to leave. He laughs. "I don't have to pay you more," he says. "There are many Mexicans out there just like you. If you don't like it here, go back to Mexico. I can find another busboy. Or should I call the INS?"

Julio is afraid of the INS. He doesn't want them to find him. They will send him home. His brother Tomas sometimes writes from Mexico. Tomas doesn't tell Julio to come home. They're very poor. Life in their village is still very difficult.

Tomas had a letter from Francisca. He tells Julio about the letter. Francisca is somewhere in California. But Julio doesn't know where or how to find her.

So Julio stays in Seguin. He's not happy, and he's not unhappy. He has friends and a place to live. In some ways, he feels at home. Although Pedro pays him badly, Julio is learning a lot. He can do most of the jobs around the restaurant. In fact, he can do almost anything. But he cannot speak English.

After You Read

1. Write *Y* (yes), *N* (no), or *M* (maybe) before these statements. If you write *M*, explain your answer to the class.

__N__ 1. Julio finds his sister Francisca in San Angelo.

____ 2. Francisca knew that Julio was coming to America.

____ 3. Alec Martin gives Julio a ride to Seguin.

_____ 4. Julio stays in Seguin for seven years.

_____ 5. Julio will find his sister Francisca.

_____ 6. Julio will always live in Seguin.

2. **Write the word opposite in meaning from the given word or words.**

bad-tempered	unopened	slowly
exhausted	crying	
hopeless	heavy	

1. __unopened__ opened

2. __________ light

3. __________ wide awake

4. __________ quickly

5. __________ friendly

6. __________ laughing

7. __________ hopeful

3. **Write about the story (Chapters 1–4) in your own words. Look back at the chapters for vocabulary ideas. Use a piece of paper. Then exchange your paper with someone else in the class.**

4. **Discuss the question below with your classmates. Make notes on what you decide.**
   - What kind of person is Alec Martin? How do you know?

5. **Pretend you are Julio. Tell the class how you feel as you travel to Seguin. OR: Have you ever done something not knowing what will happen? Tell the class, or write about your experience.**

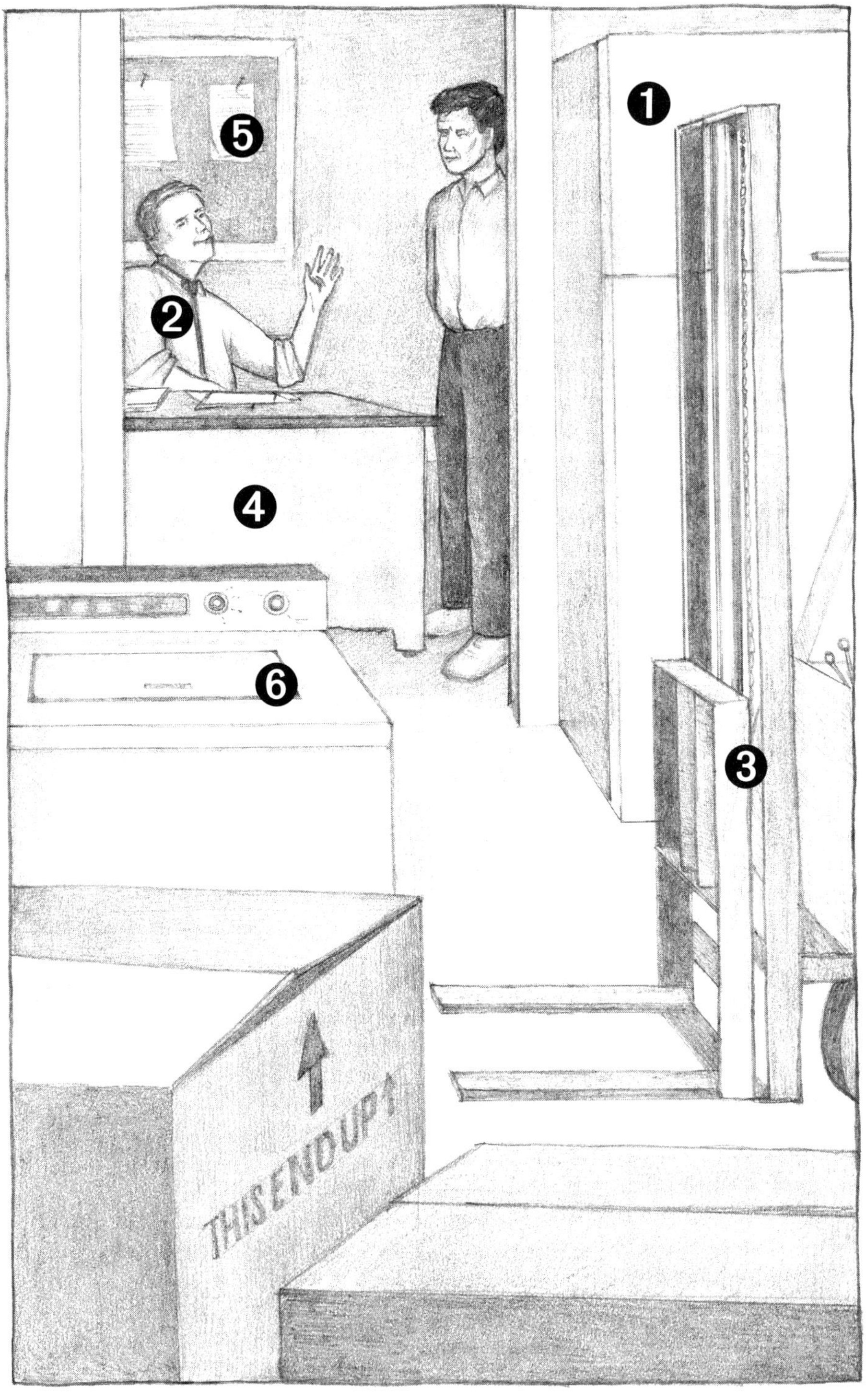
1
5
2
4
6
3
THIS END UP

Chapter 5

Amnesty

Before You Read

1. **Discuss these questions with your classmates:**
   - What do you know about the amnesty program?
   - What do these words and phrases mean?

amnesty	exploit
border	permanent resident status
legally	temporary resident status

   - What is a temporary residence card? Look at the picture on page 32. Julio is talking to the INS officer. Match the numbers on the picture with words and phrases below.

_____ counter	_____ INS officer
_____ temporary residence card	

2. **Look at the picture on page 30. Julio is talking to his boss, Travis Coombes, in the warehouse. Julio has worked there for a few months. Match the numbers on the picture with the words and phrases below:**

_____ desk	_____ refrigerator
_____ washing machine	_____ Travis Coombes
_____ loading cart	_____ papers

3. **Think about the picture and answer these questions:**
   - Look at the way Julio and Travis Coombes are talking.

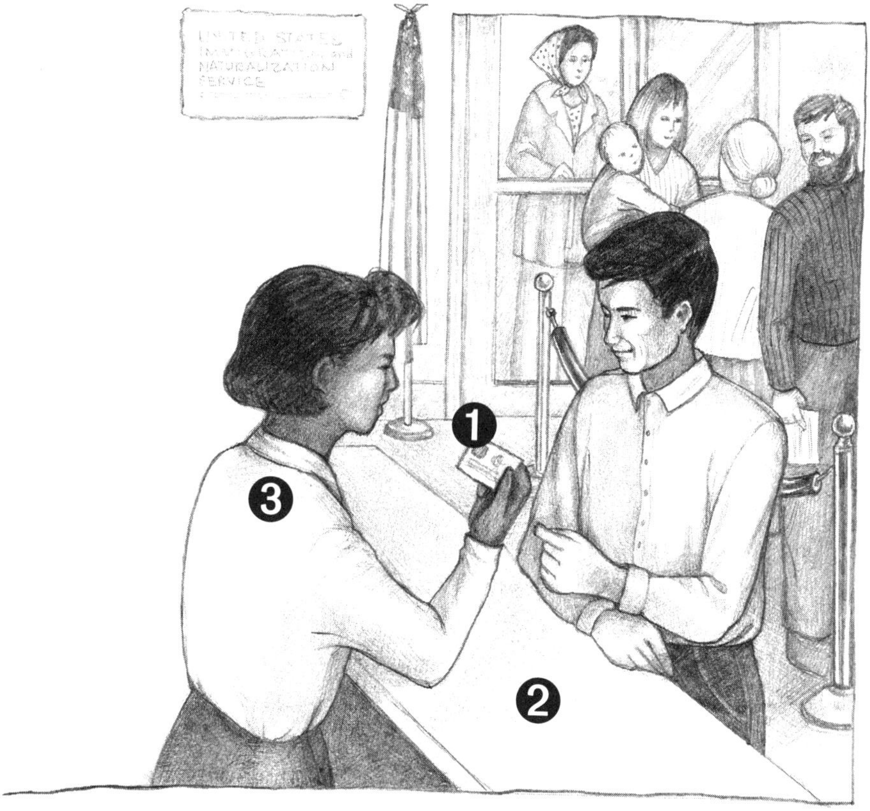

How do you know who the boss is?

- What kind of person is Travis Coombes?

Amnesty

Julio and his friend Juan are in the restaurant kitchen. They're cleaning up after dinner. Pedro is standing in a corner nearby. He's watching them work.

"Do you know about the amnesty program?" Juan asks Julio.

Pedro moves closer to hear what Juan and Julio are saying.

"What's amnesty?" asks Julio.

Pedro crosses his arms and smiles.

"I heard about it on the Spanish radio station," Juan says. "We can apply for temporary residence cards. If we've been here for five years, we can stay. The INS says we can work legally."

From behind them, Pedro laughs. "Sure, sure, boys. Don't you believe it!" he says. "Do you really think the INS is going to help you? They'll get your names and send you back to Mexico."

Juan looks worried. Julio doesn't speak.

"You'd better be careful," Pedro goes on. "If you apply for amnesty, I can't help you."

"Help us?" The idea makes Julio laugh. "You won't be able to *exploit* us, you mean," he thinks. "We work hard, and you pay us next to nothing. Amnesty will help us."

Julio and Juan say no more. But Julio decides to find out about amnesty.

He listens to the Spanish radio and reads the Spanish-language newspaper. He discovers a lot of things.

First he must show that he came to America before January 1, 1982. Then the government will let him work. He will have temporary resident status. After eighteen months, he can apply for permanent resident status. As part of the amnesty program, he must learn English.

One day, Pedro finds Julio listening to the radio. "Forget it!" he says. "Where will you find an English teacher? Things cost money, my boy."

Julio thinks about amnesty a lot. What if Pedro is right? What if it isn't true? Maybe the INS *will* send him back to Mexico.

But Julio keeps on listening to the radio. He learns more. There are free English classes in Houston. Julio decides to go there. He talks his plan over with Juan.

"Why Houston? Why not San Antonio?" Juan asks.

"I want to make a fresh start," Julio says, "Houston is a new place. I can begin a new life."

"Good luck," Juan says. "I'm not going. I think Pedro is right. You'll be back in Mexico in a week."

Julio tells Pedro about his plan. "I am going to go to Houston."

Pedro just laughs at him. He doesn't believe Julio will really go.

Julio gets ready to leave. He finds someone to drive him to Houston. He puts a few things into a suitcase. He places his mother's gold brooch in a small bag. "Will I ever see Francisca again?" he wonders.

One week later, Julio is ready to go. He collects his last paycheck. Then he goes to say good-bye.

Pedro is furious. "You ungrateful dog!" he yells. "Who gave you food and a place to sleep? You had nothing! You owe me, Julio!"

Julio says good-bye to Juan, then turns and walks away. He wanted Pedro to send his mail to him in Houston. Now he doesn't want to ask him for anything. He doesn't even want him to know his new address. Not that he has a place to go.

Julio goes out to meet his ride. He feels the way he did at Big Bend seven years ago. He's scared and anxious, like the time when Francisca didn't meet him. But he's excited, too.

At 6:00 A.M., Julio arrives in Houston. He goes straight to the Legalization Center. A lot of people are already there.

At 8:00 A.M. the doors open. Julio goes in and takes a number. There are several people in line. He talks to them while he's waiting. One person tells him about a room for rent. Julio asks for the address.

At 3:00 P.M., someone finally calls Julio's number. He sees an INS officer. The INS officer tells him about free English lessons. He writes down the address.

By 5:00 P.M. Julio has a temporary residence card. He can work without being afraid!

Julio goes to look at the room. It's small and hot, but he takes it. Then he goes out to find some food. He buys a Spanish newspaper.

His money is going fast. He has to find a job.

The next morning Julio looks for work. It's not easy. Most of the good jobs require English.

At last, after a week, Julio finds a job. He'll work in a

warehouse, moving refrigerators and washing machines. The name of his new boss is Travis Coombes.

The next week, Julio begins evening English classes.

The weeks go by. Julio is enjoying his life. His job is going well, and he likes his English class. He's often very tired, but he's learning.

Travis likes to see Julio at work. "You're a good worker," Travis tells Julio in Spanish. "And you're smart. You think. You use your brain. It's hard to keep smart guys like you."

"You don't have to speak Spanish to me, Mr. Coombes," Julio says. Travis Coombes's Spanish is not very good. He learned it twenty years ago in high school.

"Oh, so you understand English?" Travis Coombes asks. He seems surprised. "Of course you do. You take those classes at night, don't you?" He doesn't sound pleased. "Okay, Julio, we'll try it."

From then on, Travis Coombes speaks to Julio in English. Travis watches and listens carefully to see what Julio understands.

At the end of the month, Julio's schedule changes. His new shift starts at 4:00 P.M.

Julio goes to see Travis Coombes. "I can't work nights, sir," he says respectfully. "I need to go to English class."

Travis Coombes looks up from his desk. "Sorry, Julio," he says. "I need you here at night."

"I can come in on Friday and Saturday nights." Julio offers. "But I can't come Monday through Thursday. I'll miss class."

Travis Coombes smiles lazily. "Now that's too bad, isn't it?" he says. "I need you here Monday through Thursday nights. You'll be okay. After all, I can speak Spanish. You don't need to learn English."

Something about Travis reminds Julio of Pedro Vazquez.

After You Read

1. Write *T* if the statement is true and *F* if it's false. If the statement is false, write the true answer below it.

____ 1. Julio goes to Houston.

____ 2. Pedro Vazquez wants Julio to leave.

____ 3. Julio finds work the day he arrives in Houston.

____ 4. Julio's job is in a warehouse.

____ 5. Julio's boss is Travis Coombes.

____ 6. Travis Coombes speaks excellent Spanish.

____ 7. Julio enjoys his English class.

2. Complete each sentence with one of the two-word verbs below:

apply for	clean up
find out	keep on
qualify for	remind of
talk over	

1. When you *discuss something,* you **talk** it **over**.

2. When you *continue* doing something, you ________ doing it.

3. When somebody *makes you remember* somebody else, they ________ you ________ them.

4. When you *want to get a job,* you ________ it.

5. When you *learn about something,* you ________ about it.

6. When you *make things clean and orderly again,* you

   ________ .

7. When you *have the right qualities for something,* you

   ________ it.

3. Find the answer to this question in Chapter 5:

- What does Julio have to do to qualify for amnesty?

____

____

____

____

____

____

____

____

____

____

4. Discuss the questions below with your classmates. Make notes on what you decide.

- Is Pedro right to feel furious at Julio? Has Julio treated him badly? Or, has Pedro treated Julio badly?

5. Think about these questions. Then, role-play the situation with a classmate. One person can be Julio and the other, his friend. The friend is giving advice to Julio.

- Why does Travis Coombes want Julio to miss his English class?
- What advice would you give Julio?

CLEANEI
CLOSED
HELP
WANTED
1
2
3
4
5
6

Chapter 6

A Change of Job

Before You Read

1. **Discuss these questions with your classmates:**
   - Have you ever changed jobs? Why?
   - What makes a good employer? What makes a bad boss?
   - What do these words mean?

decision	pay (noun)
personnel office	schedule

2. **Look at the picture on page 38. Julio and Carolina are outside the dry cleaner's. Match the numbers on the picture with the words and phrases below:**

_____ Help Wanted sign	_____ store hours
_____ Carolina	_____ rack for clothes
_____ counter	_____ office

3. **Think about the picture and answer these questions:**
   - What do people do in a dry-cleaning business?
   - What time of day is it? How do you know?

4. **Look at the picture on page 40. What does it tell you?**

A Change of Job

"You don't really need me all those nights," Julio replies quietly.

"Are you calling me a liar?" Travis Coombes asks.

Julio waits to find the right words. He would like to argue with this man.

"I'm not calling you a liar, Mr. Coombes," he says slowly. "But you have a reason for putting me on the night shift. You don't want me to learn English. Why?"

Travis Coombes looks away. "You don't need English here," he repeats. "I can speak Spanish. That's enough."

Julio is very angry. Travis can see how mad he feels. Travis says, "Anyway, the new schedule doesn't start until Monday. You can still go to your English class tonight." He turns away and walks off.

Julio attends his English class that night. He's still upset. He wonders what his classmates would think of his boss.

Toward the end of the hour Julio's teacher, Sandi Kleeman, asks, "We have a few more minutes. Does anyone have any questions?"

Julio raises his hand. The class is sitting in a circle. He can see everyone easily.

"My boss wants to put me on the night shift," he says. His voice is still angry. "I'll have to miss class."

Several students turn to Julio. "That's too bad," someone says. "What are you going to do?"

"I don't know," Julio says. "I need the job. But I need to improve my English, too."

Everyone understands. A student asks, "Can you get your boss to change the schedule?"

"I already tried," Julio says. "My boss says he needs me at night. But that's not true. He just doesn't want me to learn English. He thinks I'll leave when I learn English.

"My other boss, in Seguin, was the same way," Julio continues. "He didn't want me to try for amnesty. He paid us very little, and I was afraid to ask for more. Now this guy wants me to work like a horse and not learn English. And without English, I'll never get a better job."

“You can leave,” a woman says. “There are lots of other jobs.”

Julio turns around to look. It’s Carolina Rangel. She’s a smart student. Carolina usually has something good to say.

“Do you have an idea, Carolina?” Ms. Kleeman asks.

“Yes, I do,” Carolina says. “I saw a ‘Help Wanted’ sign at the dry cleaners near where I work. With a job like that, you’ll have to speak English. Nobody uses Spanish around there.”

The teacher looks at her watch. “It’s time for our break,” she says. “I hope you can stay with us, Julio. You’re learning a lot.”

Julio follows Carolina out of the classroom. “Can you tell me more about that job? Where is the dry cleaner’s?”

“I don’t known the exact address,” Carolina says. “I pass it on my way home.”

“Can I take the bus with you tonight?” Julio asks. He feels a little uncomfortable. “I know you have a job. But do you have to work tonight?”

“No, I’m free tonight,” Carolina replies. “I don’t have to look after the children. Mr. and Mrs. Elliot want me to learn English. They correct my grammar and encourage me. They give me time off for my classes.”

“You’re lucky,” Julio says. “My bosses have never helped me with my English.”

“I think it depends on the employer, what he or she needs,” Carolina says. “I’m a live-in baby-sitter. The Elliots want their little boy to hear good English. I’m with him all the time, so they want me to speak well.”

After class, Julio leaves with Carolina. She shows him where she works. Then, she points out the dry cleaner’s building. Julio writes down the address.

That night, Julio feels hopeful. Maybe he will find a new job.

Julio thinks about Travis Coombes. What will he say to him? He tries hard to think. But it’s difficult. Whenever he closes his eyes, Carolina’s face appears. He sees her eyes, the way her hair falls …

Julio feels in his pocket. Inside is a small piece of paper. Carolina's telephone number is written on it.

The next day Julio goes to the dry cleaner's. He speaks to the manager. He asks and answers many questions. At the end of the conversation, Julio has a job. The hours are 8:00 to 5:00. His evenings will be free. Now he must tell Travis Coombes.

"I have to leave this job," Julio tells his boss, a day later. "I'm giving you two weeks' notice."

"Do you mean it?" Travis Coombes asks. "Do you have another job?"

"Yes, I do," Julio replies. "I'll be working for a dry-cleaning business."

Travis Coombes starts to laugh. "That's real man's work," he says. "All those heavy loads of clothes. You're strong, Julio. Why take a job like that?"

"Because I'll be able to use my English," Julio answers, "And they'll let me continue my class."

"The money's probably no good," Travis Coombes says. "But have it your own way. Go and see personnel."

Julio goes to the personnel office and tells them his news. Travis is right about one thing. The pay at the warehouse is much better than the pay at the dry cleaner's.

Julio worries about his decision. Did he do the right thing? He must learn English quickly. He will practice English at the dry cleaner's.

And Carolina Rangel works nearby ...

After You Read

1. Circle the best word to complete each sentence.

Travis Coombes (1) (*helps depends on does not want*) Julio to learn English. He changes Julio's (2) (*class job schedule*) to the night shift. Julio tells his (3) (*classmates employer personnel*) about his problem. One student, Carolina, tells Julio about a job at the (4) (*baby-sitters dry cleaner's warehouse.*) The (5) (*notice pay time off*) is less, but the (6) (*decision clothes hours*) are good.

2. Match the words in column A with their meanings in column B.

A	**B**
1. liar	a. not light
2. heavy	b. fight with words
3. improve	c. unhappy or angry
4. argue	d. someone who doesn't tell the truth
5. encourage	e. available time
6. upset	f. get better
7. miss	g. give help
8. free time	h. not to have

3. Look over Chapter 6 to find the answers to the questions below. Time yourself to see how fast you can finish.

- Where do you first see Carolina Rangel's name?

  Line number __________.

- What is the name of Julio's English teacher?

  ____

  ____

- Who does Carolina work for?

  ____

  ____

Time: __________

4. **Discuss the questions below with your classmates. Make notes on what you decide.**
   - What's better about Julio's new job? What's worse?
   - What makes a job "good"?

5. **Write your own sentences about these people in the story:**

   Julio and Travis Coombes:

   ____

   ____

   ____

   ____

   Julio and Carolina:

   ____

   ____

   ____

   ____

   - What do you think will happen between Julio and Carolina?

3
6
2
7
5
4
1

Chapter 7

Ups and Downs

Before You Read

1. **Discuss these questions with your classmates:**
   - Did you ever lose a job? How did you feel?

2. **Look at the picture on page 46. Julio is in his room. Match the numbers on the picture with the words below:**

   _____ brooch _____ wallet _____ TV

   _____ toaster oven _____ watch

   _____ letter _____ dresser

3. **Think about the picture and answer this question:**
   - How does Julio look?

4. **Look at the picture on page 48. Julio is talking to Carolina on the telephone. Think about the picture and answer these questions:**
   - What's happening in the picture?
   - How does Carolina feel?

Ups and Downs

The day before he leaves, Julio buys a TV and a toaster oven. He gets a good price because he still works for the warehouse.

He begins his new job and enjoys going to class every evening. It's easier now because he's not so tired. He sees Carolina at every class. She helps him with his English. On weekends, they sometimes go to the movies together.

One night, Julio picks up Carolina and meets her employers,

Don and Wendy Elliot. They are nice people, but rather quiet. They both work, so Carolina looks after their son, Wesley. He's almost two years old. Wendy Elliot is pregnant. She's expecting the new baby in a few months. Carolina is excited. She seems to like her baby-sitting job.

At the end of their English course, Julio and Carolina take an examination. They both pass. Their school will be closed for a week. Julio wonders about signing up for the next level of English classes.

"I'm going to do it," Carolina says. "I want to get my GED."

"What's the GED?" Julio asks.

"It's the general education diploma," Carolina explains. "It's for people like me who didn't finish high school."

"What will you do when you get it?" Julio wants to know.

"I'm not sure," Carolina replies. "But it will help me do all kinds of things. Maybe I'll go on to college."

Julio isn't so sure that he wants to continue with classes. He knows enough English now to apply for permanent residence. But he wants to make more money. The job at the dry cleaner's doesn't pay well. And it's boring. All he does is take in dirty clothes and give back clean ones.

He writes to Tomas and receives a letter back. "I'm glad you wrote," Tomas writes. "I sent a letter to Seguin, but I had no reply. Now I know why.

"Francisca is in Galveston, near Houston. She'd like to see you.

"We are all well. Nothing is new here. Life must be very different for you."

Julio looks at the letter and thinks about Tomas. Tomas is right. Life is very different. The biggest difference is Carolina!

Julio sits in his room and thinks. He decides to visit Francisca. He will go to Galveston this weekend.

Julio takes out the brooch and looks at it. He remembers his mother. In his mind he sees her getting ready for church, wearing the gold brooch. Sadly, he puts the brooch down on his dresser.

Julio watches some television programs in English, then goes to bed.

In the middle of the night, he wakes up suddenly. Something cold is pressing against his neck.

"Don't move," a man's voice says, "and you won't get hurt."

Julio thinks quickly. What is happening? He tries to turn his head. A knife point presses harder into his neck. Julio feels a small pain.

"I told you not to move," the man says. "I mean it!"

Julio lies still. The man with the knife stays with him. Julio hears someone else in the room. Then the footsteps leave. "There are at least two of them," he thinks. He tries to think what to do.

Then from outside come two knocks on the door. The man with the knife gets up and runs out of the room.

Julio jumps up and rushes to the door. He hears a car start, but he can't see. It's too dark. The car is lost in the night.

Julio turns on the light. His TV and the toaster oven are gone. So are his watch and wallet. And where is his mother's brooch? They took that, too!

Julio calls his landlady, and she dials 911. The police arrive in a few minutes.

They listen to Julio's story. "There was nothing you could do," one officer says. "You were asleep; they were awake. And one of them had a knife. No, Mr. Martinez, you did the right thing."

"Will I get my things back?" Julio asks. He's holding a handkerchief to his neck. There's a little blood where the knife cut him.

The officer shakes her head. "I doubt it," she says. "They sell those things quickly. Of course, we'll watch the stores and let you know if something turns up."

Julio feels miserable. Why did they have to take his mother's brooch? And why didn't he hide it? He usually did.

Julio calls Carolina the next morning, but there's no answer. He feels really bad. He needs to speak to her.

That afternoon, Julio's boss, Mrs. Figari, calls her two employees into the office.

"I have bad news," she tells them. "The owners decided to sell their dry-cleaning business. They're going to close this store. We can't accept any more orders. I'll make sure the people get their clothes back."

"But what about us?" Julio asks.

"You're out of a job, I'm afraid. You get two weeks' pay. I'm sorry," Mrs. Figari says. She turns away. She's upset, too.

Julio can't believe it. Robbed last night, out of work today!

He calls Carolina again. This time she answers. He tells her about the robbery and his job.

"Oh, Julio, that's awful," she says. "I'm really sorry."

Julio hears a child crying. It's probably Wesley.

"Can I see you tonight?" Julio asks.

"I can't," Carolina says, "not tonight." Her voice sounds worried. "Wendy was at the hospital all morning. She has to stay in bed." The crying goes on.

"Wesley can't understand, and he's frightened," Carolina explains. "Don is on a plane right now, but he won't be home until late. I can't go out. They need me here."

Julio hangs up the phone and thinks, "I need you, too." Then he gets on a bus to go home.

As he rides, he feels himself getting more and more angry. Angry at the robbers, angry about his job, and furious at Carolina.

"What does she care about me?" he thinks. "All she cares about is that family. So what? There are other people I can talk to."

After You Read

1. Number these sentences in the correct order (1–5).

_____ Two men enter Julio's room during the night.

_____ Julio buys a TV and a toaster oven.

_____ Julio calls Carolina, but she can't see him.

_____ Julio goes to work and learns that he has no job.

_____ Julio plans to visit Francisca in Galveston.

2. Find words in Chapter 7 to complete the sentences below:

1. Wendy Elliot is going to have a baby. She's __________ .
2. Carolina and Julio took an __________ at the end of their English course.
3. The police officer doesn't think Julio will get his things back. "I __________ it," the officer says.
4. Julio works for the dry cleaner. He's one of the __________ .
5. Mrs. Figari is sad about the store closing. She's __________, too.
6. Two people took Julio's things from him. They __________ him.

3. Retell Chapter 7 in your own words. Look back through the chapter for vocabulary and ideas.

____

____

____

____

____

4. **Discuss the question below with your classmates:**
   - How can you stop people from stealing from you? Make a list of suggestions.

5. **Has anyone ever robbed you? What happened? How did you feel? Tell the class, or write about your experience.**

ALARM
1
2
3
4
5
6

Chapter 8

From Bad to Worse

Before You Read

1. **Discuss these questions with your classmates:**
   - What do these expressions mean?

     to feel sorry for yourself
     to make a fool of yourself

   - How could Julio make a fool of himself?

2. **Show your classmates what you do when you**

lean over	lurch
rise unsteadily	trip

3. **Look at the picture on page 54. Julio is throwing up in the garden outside the house where Carolina works. Match the numbers on the picture with the words and phrases below:**

_____ flower bed	_____ lights
_____ window	_____ hose
_____ sprinkler	_____ burglar alarm

4. **Think about the picture and answer these questions?**
   - What has happened?
   - What will Carolina do or say? How will she feel?

From Bad to Worse

Julio stops at the cantina near his home. He's not ready to return to his room, not yet. He finds a dark corner and sits down.

He starts to look at his watch for the time. But, of course, he doesn't have a watch anymore.

The clock over the bar says that it's 5:00 P.M.

A lot of people are near the bar. It's noisy. Julio avoids the bar and the people. He wants to be alone. He orders a beer from the waitress. Then he sits and drinks and feels sorry for himself.

Five hours later, Julio decides to call Carolina. He's feeling drunk and can't stand up too well. He has trouble putting the money into the pay phone.

"Maybe I'll go visit her," he says to himself. "It's only ten o'clock. She'll be awake. She can tell me if she cares about me. I have a lot of problems. She'll feel sorry for me."

Julio rises unsteadily and goes out into the street. The buses run until midnight. He can easily go to see Carolina.

At 10:30 P.M., Julio arrives at the Elliots' house. There are no lights on inside. "They must already be asleep," Julio thinks.

Don Elliot's car is in the driveway. "Good," Julio thinks. "He can look after his wife. Then Carolina can come out with me."

Julio moves toward the house. A garden hose is lying in the grass. Julio trips over it.

He gets up again, very carefully. He doesn't want to wake up everybody. He just wants to see Carolina.

Her room is at the back of the house. But there's a problem. All the windows are shut. How will Carolina hear him?

Julio picks up a little stone. He throws it at Carolina's window. The stone misses. It hits the house instead.

"I need a bigger stone," Julio thinks. "A bigger one will work." He looks around the garden and finds a large rock. He throws again.

This time he hits the window all right. There's the sound of glass breaking. Then he hears the burglar alarm go off. In the house, lights go on. Outside, lights come on, too. Julio smiles. It's like being on stage, giving a performance.

All at once, Julio feels sick. His head is cold and wet. His stomach is moving in a strange way.

Carolina looks out her window. She sees Julio. His back is to her. He's leaning over the flower bed, throwing up.

Julio doesn't remember much after that, only bits and pieces. He knows that Don Elliot told him to go home. He took Julio to the bus stop. Don looked tired and seemed to be angry.

Julio saw Carolina for only a second. She came downstairs and opened the door. But when Julio tried to speak to her, she slammed it in his face.

Now Carolina isn't talking to him.

Julio calls Don Elliot the next day and apologizes. "I'd like to pay for the window," he offers. "I can come out and fix it."

"It's all done, thank you," Don says.

Julio spends every day looking for a job. He cuts grass for a few days. He delivers notices for another day. The jobs pay something, but they're not the jobs Julio wants.

"I wish I could find something steady and permanent," he thinks. "I work hard. I should be able to get something better than this."

English classes are starting again. Julio attends the first one. A new teacher is there. Ms. Kleeman will be absent for a few evenings. Julio doesn't like the new teacher.

Carolina is in the class. She listens closely to the teacher. She doesn't look at Julio. She doesn't even see him!

Julio feels hurt and angry. He tries not to think about Carolina. He talks to the other students in the class, especially the young women. He listens to them and laughs at their jokes.

"Maybe Carolina is watching me," he thinks. But he's not sure.

After class, Julio sits in his room and thinks some more.

He doesn't want to go to Galveston. Why go there? He doesn't have the brooch. Anyway, he thinks angrily, Francisca can come to see him. What does she care?

Should he return to Seguin? He could work someplace else. He knows enough English now. But would Pedro give him a job? Would Travis Coombes take him back?

Maybe he should just return to Mexico. Why stay in Houston, where nobody cares?

After You Read

1. Write *Y* (yes), *N* (no), or *M* (maybe) before these statements. If you write *M*, explain your answer to the class.

_____ 1. Julio drinks too much in the cantina.

_____ 2. Julio tries to speak with Carolina.

_____ 3. Julio fixes the window.

_____ 4. Carolina is angry with Julio.

_____ 5. Julio will return to Mexico.

_____ 6. Julio is angry with himself.

2. Match the words in column A with their meanings in column B.

A	B
1. noisy	a. had too much to drink
2. bits and pieces	b. unchanging, not temporary
3. slam	c. shut very hard
4. apologize	d. not quiet
5. drunk	e. a few things, this and that
6. permanent	f. say you're sorry

3. **With a group, show Julio's actions so far in the story. Draw the story like a graph. Put the happy, positive things at the top. Put the unhappy, negative things at the bottom. Connect the events with lines.**

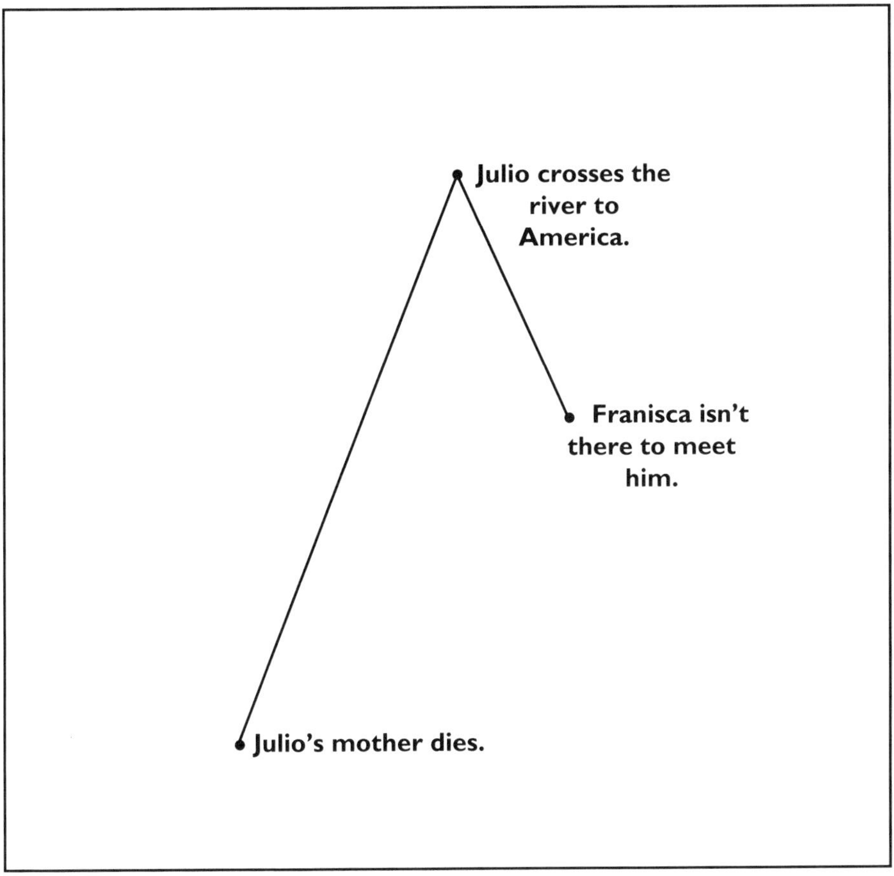

4. **Discuss the question below with a classmate. Make notes on what you decide. Share your answers with the class.**
   - What will happen between Julio and Carolina now?

5. **Pretend that you are Carolina's friend. What can you say to her? Role-play the situation with a classmate. One student can be Carolina, and the other can be her friend. OR: What advice do you have for Julio? Tell the class, or write about it.**

Chapter 9

Other People's Problems

Before You Read

1. Discuss these questions with your classmates:

- What is a personal problem?
- Is it a good idea to talk about your problems?

2. What do these words and phrases mean?

appendix	control yourself	depressed
gasp	mixed feelings	operation

2. Look at the picture on page 60. Agatha is telling her story to the class. Think about the picture and answer these questions:

- How old is Agatha?
- Are the students listening attentively? Are they sympathetic?

3. Look at the picture on page 62. Agatha's son Reuben is at work.

- What does a construction company do?
- What is workman's compensation? What helps pay if you are hurt at work?

Match the number on the pictures with the words below:

_____ safe _____ loading cart

_____ box _____ Reuben

4. Think about the picture and answer these questions:

- What's Reuben carrying? How heavy is it? Is he doing something dangerous?

1
2
3
4

Other People's Problems

Julio feels lonely, so he returns to English class. He has mixed feelings: He wants to learn, but he's depressed. English class isn't fun anymore. He misses his old teacher, Ms. Kleeman.

Only ten people are in the class now. One evening Sandi Kleeman comes back. Carolina speaks to her before class. Julio sees them talking, but he can't hear what they're saying.

"We're so glad you're back," a student tells Sandi. "We missed you a lot. Why did you leave?"

Sandi laughs. "I didn't want to," she says, "but I had to have an operation. I had my appendix out. It's a simple medical procedure, but I had to rest and get well. I'm fine now!"

The class prepares to read a story. It's about personal problems. "Well, I told you my story," Sandi says. "What about you? What's a problem, anyway?"

"Like when your car breaks down," someone says.

"Or you have an operation," someone else adds.

Sandi nods, then looks around the room. "What about you, Julio?" she asks.

Julio looks up. "What did Carolina say?" Julio wonders. "Were they talking about me?" He says aloud, "There's nothing I want to talk about." The words sound rude.

Sandi Kleeman looks quickly at him. Then somebody else starts to speak.

It's Agatha Romero. "Please, I have to talk," she says. The students turn to look at her.

Agatha Romero is older than the other students. She's always busy and usually arrives just as class is starting. Julio knows her a little. She comes from Guatemala. Now she wants to talk.

"Go ahead, Agatha," Ms. Kleeman says. Everyone waits for Agatha to begin.

"We came here from Guatemala," Agatha says. "At first, everything was hard. We were afraid of the INS. Every time I went to buy food, I worried. What if the INS was there? What if they caught me? And if my husband was late home, I cried. Did the INS catch him?"

Everyone in class is quiet. They all know about the INS.

"Then we got amnesty," Agatha goes on. "It was like being free! It was like coming out of a prison. We were able to work."

"Everything was good, very good. I sent a little money home. People in Guatemala City think everyone in America is rich. They think money grows on trees. It is not so, but still, I sent money home.

"My son, my big boy, Reuben, he's nineteen. He's a good boy. He speaks English and Spanish, but he hated school. So, we say, okay Reuben, leave school, take a job. Your little brother and your sisters will stay at school. Maybe they will get an education."

She pauses and looks around the room. Everyone is listening.

"My son worked for a construction company. They build shopping centers and office buildings. The money was okay, the work was hard, it was a job. He was happy.

"One day, the boss told Reuben to carry a safe into the building. You know, a safe: a metal box to keep money in. It was a big, heavy box, maybe eighty pounds.

"Reuben's a strong boy. He didn't use a cart or anything. He just picked up the safe and walked across the floor. But there was something, a box maybe, on the floor. Reuben didn't see it. He fell over it."

Agatha's voice is breaking. Carolina is sitting nearby. She offers a handkerchief and pats Agatha's arm. Agatha controls herself and continues, "He held onto that safe. But his hand, his left hand, got caught. It got caught under that big eighty-pound safe. The metal cut him, his hand, right to the bone."

Everyone gasps. They can see it all. The red blood, the white bone …

Agatha is crying now. But she stops, then goes on. She holds the handkerchief near her mouth. It's hard to hear her words clearly.

"The boss took him to the hospital. Thank God for that. And we don't have to pay for anything. The insurance will pay. It's a workman's compensation case. He was working when he fell. The doctors did what they could."

Agatha is crying hard. Carolina puts her arm around her. But there is more.

"The doctors were not quick enough," Agatha says. "Two of my son's fingers do not move. And now my boy is home. He sits around the house. He will not eat. He just looks at his left hand. He's like a little boy again. Just like a child. He wants everyone to look after him. I'm sorry. I don't know what to do."

Several students gather around Agatha. Sandi Kleeman says, "We can stop for a while. Let's take a break."

— · — · —

Class is over. Julio is getting ready to go home.

He thinks about Agatha and her story. Her story made him feel more depressed. Agatha's unhappy, but she's unhappy for somebody else. Julio feels selfish. He's not worrying about anyone else, only himself. He wonders how Carolina feels.

Julio knows that Agatha will help her son. Reuben will be able to take care of his problems.

"And I must take care of mine," Julio thinks. The students are leaving the classroom. Carolina is about to leave with them.

He hurries up to her. "I must talk with you," he says quietly. He is surprised. He feels very nervous, but his voice is strong and firm.

After You Read

1. Circle the best word to complete each sentence.

Julio goes back to (1) (*class work the hospital*). His old teacher, Ms. Kleeman, returns after (2) (*a break an operation a story*). One day a student, (3) (*Carolina Agatha Sandy*), tells a story about her (4) (*son sister husband*). Julio realizes that he's being (5) (*depressed busy selfish*), thinking only of himself. He decides that he must (6) (*forget talk to leave*) Carolina.

2. Complete each sentence with one of the words or phrases below:

breaks down	busy
control	gasp
gather around	hated
miss	mixed
rude	simple

1. He feels one way and another; his feelings are __________ .
2. The class __________ their old teacher. They wish Ms. Kleeman was there.
3. The students breathe in loudly, or __________ when Agatha finishes her story.
4. She tries to stop crying and to __________ herself.
5. Reuben didn't like school at all. He __________ it.
6. A __________ thing is not difficult.
7. She has a lot to do, she's __________ .
8. If your car stops working, it __________ .
9. *Not* to use good manners or be polite is __________ .
10. The students come together and stand near Agatha; they __________ her.

3. Discuss the questions below with your classmates. Make notes on what you decide.

- Would Carolina really talk to Sandi about Julio?
- Why does Julio think she did?

4. **With a classmate, look back through Chapter 9 and show how people sit**
   - when they're upset.

   Think about how Agatha sat when she told her story.
   - when they're trying to help someone else.

   How did Carolina help Agatha?

5. **Were you ever hurt at work? Do you know anyone who was? What happened? Tell the class, or write about it.**

BUS

Chapter 10

Happily Ever After

Before You Read

1. **Discuss these questions with your classmates:**
   - What does the chapter title mean? What does it make you think of?
   - What does a warehouse supervisor do?
   - What do people in a personnel office do?

2. **Look at the picture on page 68. Julio is watching the bus pull away. Think about the picture and answer these questions:**
   - Where is Carolina?
   - What has happened?
   - How does Julio feel?

3. **Look at the picture on page 70. It's the manager's office at the warehouse. Julio is handing Fred Williamson his work authorization card. Match the number on the picture with the words and phrases below:**

   _____ application form

   _____ file folder

   _____ filing cabinet

   _____ temporary residence card

   _____ Fred Williamson

4. **Think about the picture and answer these questions:**
   - What is a manager's job?
   - Why is the manager interested in Julio's temporary residence card?

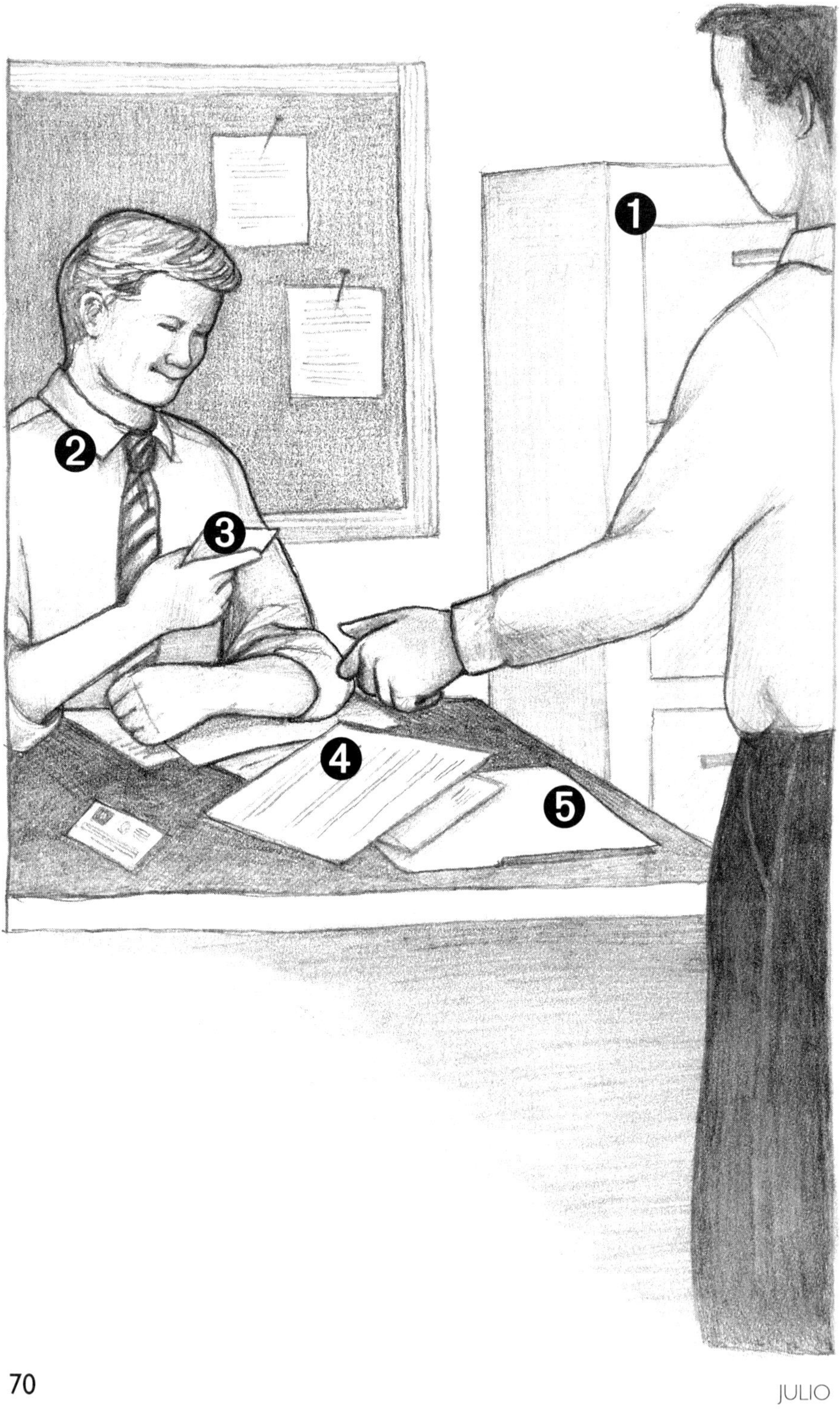
1
2
3
4
5

Happily Ever After

Julio and Carolina leave the building without speaking. Out in the street, Julio says, "I'm sorry about what happened the other night. I mean about the window and everything. I apologized to Mr. Elliot."

Carolina looks at him without saying anything. They walk on toward her bus stop.

"You're not making this easy," Julio complains.

Carolina stops short. "Why should I?" she asks. "You embarrassed me. You came out to where I work, you broke a window, and ..."

"I said I'm sorry," Julio repeats. They see the bus coming. Julio's getting nervous. He doesn't want Carolina to leave yet. The bus is getting closer and closer.

Julio takes Carolina's arm and turns her toward him. "Don't you understand?" he almost shouts. "Everything was going wrong. That night I had to see you. I need you, Carolina."

The bus pulls up at the bus stop. The door swings open.

"I know," Carolina says softly. "I need you, too, Julio." She leans forward and kisses him. Then she hurries onto the bus.

Julio can't quite believe it. What happened? Did Carolina really kiss him? He touches his lips with his fingertips to make sure. A big smile spreads across his face.

Julio doesn't take the bus home. He walks. That is, he floats. His feet feel several inches above the ground.

The next day Julio looks for work again. He buys the newspaper as usual and looks at the want ads.

A warehouse wants a supervisor. Julio looks at the address. "That's where I worked before," he thinks. "What happened to Travis Coombes? He was the supervisor there."

Julio dials the number. A secretary tells him to come for an interview that afternoon. He dresses very carefully. He's glad that he has an appointment. Will Travis Coombes remember him? Will he remember that Julio worked hard? That he gave the company two weeks' notice to find another worker? Will Travis Coombes even be there?

Julio goes to the personnel office. The clerks there recognize him. They speak to him very slowly. Julio speaks to them in English.

"Your English is much better," someone says. "That's why you left, isn't it? So you could go to English classes."

Julio nods. Then he asks, "Can you tell me anything about this job? Where is Travis Coombes?"

"The family moved to Shreveport," one clerk says. "Travis's father got sick quite suddenly. Travis left to look after his father's business. Old Mr. Coombes needed somebody with him."

"He's a good son," Julio says.

"I guess he is," the clerk says. "I never thought about it that way. Anyway, this is Travis's old job. They need a new supervisor, someone who speaks English and Spanish." She hands Julio an application form. "Fill this out," she says. "The boss will be back soon. Do you remember Mr. Williamson? He's still the manager here."

Julio waits for Mr. Williamson to return. The manager invites Julio into his office.

Fred Williamson looks at Julio. Then he looks down at Julio's application. "How good is your English?" he asks.

"I'm still taking classes," Julio says. "I can understand nearly everything and say most things. But I want to learn more."

"You might be right for this job," Mr. Williamson says. He takes out a folder. "You're strong and a good worker, it says here. Travis wrote that. It also says that you have a temporary residence card. May I see it?"

Julio hands the card to Mr. Williamson. It's the one he received at the Legalization Center in Houston. Fred Williamson looks at it carefully.

"Looks good to me," he says. He closes the folder. "The job is yours, Julio. When do you want to start?"

"Now," Julio replies, smiling. "But there's one thing, Mr. Williamson. I can't work Monday to Thursday evenings between 5:30 and 9:30 P.M."

Fred Williamson looks surprised. "Why not?"

"My English class meets from 6:00 to 9:00 P.M. I need half an hour to get there."

Fred Williamson thinks about it. Julio feels nervous. Is the job still his?

"Well, that should be all right," Fred Williamson says. "We don't get many deliveries after four o'clock. But if there's a sudden, unexpected order, you'll have to come in."

"That's okay with me," Julio says. He signs the papers Fred Williamson gives him. At last he's back at work.

That night, Julio calls Carolina. He's eager to tell her about his new job.

He picks her up from the Elliots' and they talk for a long time. They discuss their plans and hopes. They decide they want to marry and to be together. The future looks very bright.

"And some day," Julio laughs, "we're going to find my sister Francisca. But first of all we'll send photographs of you to Tomas."

"Are you going to say 'we' instead of 'I' from now on?" Carolina laughs.

Julio looks at her dark eyes and says seriously, "I hope so. I don't ever want to do anything without you."

Carolina smiles her quiet smile.

After You Read

1. Number these sentences in the correct order (1–5):

_____ Carolina kisses Julio and runs to the bus.

______ Julio gets the job of supervisor.

______ Julio and Carolina decide to get married.

______ Julio calls the warehouse to ask about a job.

______ Julio goes to the personnel office and fills out an application.

2. Circle the phrases (a, b, or c) closest in meaning to the underlined phrases below:

1. You <u>embarrassed</u> me.

   a. hurried

   b. made me feel small

   c. made me feel happy

2. "You're not making this easy," Julio <u>complains</u>.

   a. says angrily

   b. says quietly

   c. says unhappily

3. The clerks there <u>recognize</u> him.

   a. forget

   b. hear

   c. know

4. Mr. Williamson <u>invites</u> Julio into his office.

   a. takes

   b. asks

   c. brings

5. a sudden unexpected order

   a. something we did not know about

   b. something that will make a lot of money

   c. something we don't want

6. He is eager to tell her the news.

   a. in a hurry

   b. in no hurry

   c. afraid

7. The future looks very bright.

   a. clean

   b. cheerful

   c. colorful

3. With your classmates, list the most important events in the story. Identify the things that Julio did. You may look back at the other chapters. Then compare lists.

____

____

____

____

____

____

____

____

4. **Think about Julio and Carolina. Will they be happy together? Write a story about their life ten years from now.**

5. **What makes a good marriage? Tell the class, or write your opinions.**